WHISPERS
OF
HOPE

PAWS,
POSSIBILITIES,
& DISH

Cyndi Whatif

Award Winning Author of *Health Backwards*

Purple Beaver Publishing
Alvin. Texas 77512

Whiskers of Hope: Paws, Possibilities, & DISH
Copyright © 2023 by Cynthia May Wilson

For information, contact Purple Beaver Publishing, PO Box 1114, Alvin, TX 77512 or contact@purplebeaverpublishing.com

Library of Congress Control Number: 2023923557

ISBN(s). paperback: 979-8-9886104-5-8, eBook: 979-8-9886104-6-5
First paperback edition: December 2023
Edited by Stuart Budgen
Cover art and layout by Purple Beaver Publishing

Disclaimer: This memoir includes references to individuals whose names have been either omitted or altered to protect their privacy. The events and anecdotes recounted in this book are based on the author's recollections and interpretation of events. The author acknowledges the importance of respecting the privacy and dignity of those whose stories are shared in these pages. Any attempt to identify specific individuals is discouraged, and readers are urged to approach the narrative with an understanding of the author's intent to preserve the anonymity of certain individuals while conveying the essence of the shared experiences.

To my fellow spoonies –

May you find hope and inspiration

Contents

Introduction

As we follow this little cat's journey, watch how understanding DISH quietly works magic that changes the feline's outcome. In this particular real-life example of DISH, I share only the implementation process of a simple case study.

DISH is a very easy concept, but implementing it can be quite difficult at times, due to the many factors involved. This book is intended as a quick example of *how* the process could look. The *why* it works and the more difficult scenarios are saved for a different book.

Please remember this is not intended as medical advice. It is just a true memoir of a kitty.

Medical Disclaimer

All content, media, and information contained in this book is for informational purposes ONLY. I am sharing my personal experience. *It is NOT intended to be personal medical advice.* Only you and your doctor know your health. Always seek professional medical advice. If you choose to act on any information in this book, you are doing so at your own risk.

This book should never be a substitute for professional medical advice from healthcare professionals. It is my personal experience.

1

Nemo Needs a Sister

I could hear my husband's voice over the phone, "We don't need another pet."

I know. I couldn't believe I was bringing it up. I'm not the pet person in the family. I knew he was right, but I couldn't help it. I felt like I wanted a kitten.

"I know you're right. Just forget I said anything."

He did. I didn't.

We already had one dog called Kihap. She was our daughter's little chiweenie. When our daughter grew up and moved out, the dog somehow ended up staying behind.

We were also down to one cat. At one point, we had three cats. I never thought I'd be the owner of three cats, but when my children's begging eyes look up at me, pleading to have their own pet, well, with six kids in the family, you end up having many pets. We also had a bird at the time. It's true; we didn't need another pet.

However, Nemo, our now only cat, looked lonely. She'd had a rough start in life. She was rescued from drowning, but her twin sister didn't make it. We had adopted her and one of her other sisters together. They played with each other so much. I'd never had two kittens at once before. It's so different than having just one. Just one was actually more of a handful it seemed.

Nemo and BB played with each other, napped with each other, and looked forward to laundry day. They would play King of the Mountain and play fight over who was allowed to be the one to sit on top of all the clean clothes the longest. When BB suddenly died, Nemo would lie down next to the laundry basket on laundry day and just be.

No, we didn't need another pet, but I felt sorry for Nemo. I would even venture to say that I think she missed the house bully—our neutered male cat, Tyson—who was the family cat when these two sisters came along. But even he was gone now.

I remembered how, about a week after BB died, Nemo tried to befriend the bully. He would start every morning by "putting her in her place." I think she wanted interaction so bad that she was willing to play his game anyway he wanted to, just so she could have another animal to interact with her. Cuddling was definitely out of the question though.

However, even Tyson was gone now. He moved out when our eldest son moved out. I don't think Tyson ever looked back.

But I think Nemo didn't like being the only cat after that. She tried to snuggle with Kihap a few times, but the old dog was just too grumpy. Whenever Nemo tried, Kihap snapped at her.

So, Nemo stopped trying.

Six months went by. Six months of her staring out the window, of not running through the house being chased, of not having someone to challenge her as she waits by the laundry basket. I watched her. I tried petting her more. I tried to ignore her being lonely and wanting a sister, but I couldn't shake the idea of getting another cat.

When I went back to visit my sisters, in our remote hometown that's surrounded by farmers, we were constantly being offered a cat. Wow, it would be so easy. If I brought a cat home with me, I would have to keep it because we lived too far away to return it.

I thought about it, and I thought about Nemo too. Nemo was so unique. So timid; so loving. No, if we ever got a cat, it would have to start out as a kitten. Besides, three more months had passed since I first had the crazy idea of getting another pet. I was starting to warm to the idea of not having one. I put it out of my mind, deciding we didn't need another cat or kitten.

But what if a kitten needed us?

2

A Gift for Daisy

It was a few days before Christmas Eve, and I was standing in the kitchen, when my eldest son called me on the phone like he usually did every morning. But this time it was different.

"Mom, there is a kitten sitting in the middle of the road. What should I do?"

"Leave it alone. It probably belongs to somebody."

"I don't think so. It is awfully small, Mom."

We shared details about the location and the kitten, and I ended up saying, "Send me a picture."

I had already accepted the decision not to get another pet by then, and I had stopped thinking about it.

He sent a picture. The kitten was tiny, and it didn't look like it was doing very well.

"Fine, bring it home. But we are not keeping it."

It's true, I really had no intention of keeping it. There was an elderly lady that lived across the street who had grown up in Montana. She was always finding stray kittens and nursing them back to health before finding a new home for them.

I hadn't seen her in her yard as often as I used to. She used to take her dog for nightly walks, but he had passed on a few months ago. Maybe this kitten would help fill the void left behind by her departed dog of over twelve years. I admit I was feeling guilty for not having gone over to visit her lately. I thought this would be a great opportunity to catch up and pass the kitten off.

I saw my son pull up into the driveway, and he came walking into the house carrying a small box with him.

"Well, where is it?"

"Here," he said as he stretched out his hand to give me the box.

I was confused. I looked in the box, and the kitten was even smaller than the picture made it look. It looked dead. It wasn't moving. It wasn't trying to escape its new captors. It wasn't meowing—it wasn't doing anything. Was it even breathing?

I scooped the smelly matted ball up into my hand. It was apparent that this little guy definitely did not have a mother taking care of it. As I brought it up to eye-level, he mouthed a meow of protest at me with no sound coming out.

I didn't even know where to begin. He felt so cold. If he hadn't mouthed at me, I would have thought he was dead.

I held him up against my chest, with the stench seeping into my clothes and wafting up to my nose. It was still pretty early in the morning. Our neighbor, Daisy, would always open her garage door about six inches from the ground to indicate she was up for the day. No sign yet.

We waited another hour. His body temperature still didn't seem to be rising. He was just as cold, and just as lifeless. I thought maybe she wouldn't mind if I woke her, since it was about the time she would usually get up. She would surely understand if she saw this poor creature.

I headed over to her house. The garage door still wasn't open. I knocked on the door, and I waited a very long time. I knew she was unable to get around easily, and if I made her get out of bed it would take even longer. I knocked again, and I waited. I looked down at the kitten in my hand. He was probably getting even colder. I think I waited ten more minutes, and then I knocked one last time, thinking that if she was at least on her way to the door, then she could holler loud enough for me to hear her. But I could hear no movement and there was still no answer.

Christmas was just around the corner; she might have gone to visit her children. Now what?

I didn't know anything about kittens that small, but I did know that if someone didn't help the poor thing soon, he was going to die.

I could say "not my problem," but it was. He was looking straight up at me with closed eyes, one of which was severely swollen. It looked like it had a huge marble shoved under his eyelid.

I went back home. I didn't know how or what to feed him, but I could at least try to get him warmer.

I barely made it through the front door before being bombarded with the remaining teenagers, who were beginning to wake up during Christmas break; each one being informed of what was going on before their eyes were even open.

I could hear the excitement in my daughter's voice as she said, "Daisy didn't take it?"

"She's not there," I said.

"What are you going to do?"

"We have to get the body temperature up," I said as I headed to the bathroom.

I placed the kitten in the bottom of the tub, and he became scared and started clawing his way around blindly, looking for higher ground.

I filled a pitcher with warm water and dumped it quickly and carefully over him three times. Each time, the water that fell off of his body and raced to the drain would change color. First it was black, then brown, then just half and half clear and muddied water. But each time, I noticed blood was present too. The warm water probably made it pee and it looked like a bladder infection of some kind. Poor thing.

I used a towel to pick him up again. He was trying desperately to put up a brave fight. I dried his little body quickly and then just allowed him to rest in the towel. I needed time to think. Besides, I'm sure standing up to the water had drained all the remaining energy he had left.

"Are you going to call the vet?"

"Yes."

I made an appointment for the afternoon.

3

No Name Kitty is Alive

"Well?" said my daughter, as she was staring wide eyed at me while I hung up my phone.

"I made an appointment for 4:00."

"Why so late?"

"The first vet I called had no openings. This vet didn't either, but they said they would try to work us in if we came around 4:00."

She looked at the ball of scrunched up towel I was holding, and I knew she was thinking the same thing as I was. *Will it still be alive by then?*

Of course, I gave into her puppy dog eyes and said, "Do you want to hold him?" Before we did the pass off, we had to locate him in the bundle so that we wouldn't accidentally drop him. The towel was so hastily wrapped around the little fellow that it was hard to tell the difference between clumped towel and kitten body.

My daughter sat down on the dining room chair and just held him. Then she said, "So, we aren't going to keep him?"

"No."

After about 30 minutes, the towel moved.

"Mom! He moved."

This caused her brothers to come running too.

She slowly opened the towel, and he popped his head out. In unison, the whole room said, "Aww…"

His ears were perked for the first time, and one eye was partially open. He didn't know where he was, but the little guy was determined to find out. As he gradually wormed his way out of the towel, my daughter moved her arms forward to let him get on the table. Once he had all four paws on the surface, he crouched down to hide and make himself smaller, if that were even possible. But his curiosity took over, and he stretched his neck in hopes of seeing where he was with one barely opened eye.

Everyone sat down in their dining room chairs for a front row view of this new entertainment. Each time someone said something, the kitten would look in their direction, unsure of where to go or what to do. They started asking all kinds of questions about him, and I came into the room and started talking.

The kitten stood up and moved quickly toward my voice, and he walked right off the table. He had no depth perception! My son caught him before he hit the floor and put him back up on the table, but that would not do.

He actually started making noise when he meowed this time. He clearly wanted me. I sat down and let him walk across to me. He beelined for my voice, crawled under my chin, and went back to sleep. This was not on my schedule today. Every time I moved him though, he went straight back to his safe spot.

"What if Daisy doesn't want the kitten? What are we going to do with him?" asked one of my sons.

"I don't know. We just have to wait and see what the vet says. But for now, make sure you wash your hands after you touch him. We don't want Nemo to get sick."

"Should we give him a name for the vet appointment?" asked my daughter.

"No! Don't give him a name," said my son as he proceeded to quote a family favorite movie. "If you give him a name, then you'll get attached to him."

"We will let Daisy name him if she wants him."

But the kitten was already growing attached to me.

We had no idea what to feed him, and he wouldn't drink anything. Who knows how long since he had done either one of those. We just had to hang on until 4:00.

4

What Else Can Be Done?

After several naps and significant cuddling, 4:00 finally arrived. I took him into the vet's office. They were expecting us. I filled out the forms. Name? We didn't give him a name. *What should I put?*

"Excuse me, do I have to fill out the name?"

"Oh, don't worry about it. Just put 'kitten' for now. How much does he weigh?"

"I don't think he weighs a pound."

The receptionist's head tilted, and her eyebrows went up. "Let me take a look." She looked into the box then back at me wide eyed. "He's so tiny!"

Many questions ensued as I waited for our no name kitty to have his turn behind the waiting room door. We waited. The tiny thing in his box and me with my thoughts. *What am I doing? Why am I doing this?*

We were ushered into the examination room, and they scooped him out of the box and placed him on the scale. Fourteen ounces. "You were right. He doesn't even weigh a pound."

During the exam, the vet looked up at me and said, "If you hadn't picked him up, this poor creature definitely would not have made it through the night."

After she finished her inspection, I was told he was a she and that she had pneumonia. The vet guessed her age at about five weeks, but because she was so malnourished, it was hard to tell. The vet proceeded to tell me that if she didn't know better, it looked like someone had thrown the kitten out of the car. She highly suspected that she may end up blind because of the trauma to one eye and the infection present in both of them. She was really hoping she could at least save one eye, but it did not look promising.

The vet gave the little girl kitty a shot to try to change the tide of the severe pneumonia infection. Meanwhile, she rattled off all the instructions about what to do and what not to do. We needed to keep the kitty away from our other pets to prevent them from getting sick, and we needed to keep her in total darkness as much as possible. By doing so, she would be more likely to open her eyes and use them. If she didn't use them soon, they would for sure be lost forever. They would seal shut from all the infections she had going on.

We would also need to wipe her eyes down regularly and open them enough to get eye drops into them several times a day and night. The vet went on to say that the little fellow would need kitten formula, as well as explaining how to feed her and when. She looked at me with that knowing look and shrugged her shoulders a little, because she knew the amount of work it was going to take for this kitten to stay alive.

I made the follow-up appointment for 48 hours later. Meanwhile, my mind was racing over how to pull all those instructions off. Good thing it was Christmas break, though I never imagined I'd be spending it doing this.

I bought the items I needed. I remember buying a small quantity of baby kitten formula because I didn't think she would stay alive long enough to eat a larger amount. I chose my daughter's bedroom, as it was the room in the house which we could keep the darkest most easily. It still wasn't very dark though, due to the Texas sun shining through. We ended up draping blankets over the window too. It helped some.

My daughter and I diligently did the 'assignments' the vet gave us, wiping her delicate eyes every two hours. We spent several minutes on each eye, trying desperately to open all sets of eyelids, until we could see the eyeball to put medicine in direct contact with it, as instructed.

She stayed alive, though she still didn't look good, and she still didn't open her eyes on her own.

When I brought her into the follow-up appointment, all the office staff were shocked that she made it this far. She definitely wasn't out of the woods yet though. She didn't want to eat, and they suspected it was because it was difficult to breathe and eat at the same time. She was currently only taking in 20% of what she should be eating at each feeding.

My final instructions were, that if she did not put on weight, she would not survive. They didn't have any other advice for us other than what we were already doing, and that wasn't working good enough. So how hard do we fight to keep her alive?

This got me thinking about my own health journey. I too was once doing everything they said to do and not getting any better. Because of that, I had started looking for new ways to reach my goal of getting my health and life back.

I looked at the little ball of fur in my hands. This nameless kitty was trusting me to fix her. Did I now need to start looking for additional ways to help her? Would what I did for me work for her too? Possibly.

Was this an opportunity to test out my new hypothesis   again?

5

From Last Days to More Days

When we returned from the vet, the family talk was leaning toward being glad we took her in. Glad that at least the last days of her life she felt loved and cared for. Okay. Fine. Death sentence. She continued without a name for another two days.

Shortly after this, I remember sitting in the dark room, with the light shining up onto the ceiling from the blocked curtains just enough for us to be able to see her sitting there. We tried feeding her, but she didn't take much as usual. This time it was different, though. She was so tired, it looked like she was giving up. She could barely keep her head up from the weight of the swollen eye and utter exhaustion I would suspect.

"Mom, why don't we start doing what you figured out?"

I had already thought about it. I was in the middle of doing a heavy edit on the fifth draft of my book, *Health Backwards*, that talks about just this. But everyone had grown so attached to this kitten already that I didn't want to be blamed for it dying. When the verdict was accepted that this would be the result by the end of the week, I wasn't as reluctant to step in when asked.

"Well, let's give it a try."

"Work your magic, Mom."

Great… talk about no pressure!

It was such a simple thing. A small thing. But animals are different to people, and some essential oils can affect pets more than they affect us. So, I did not include any of those. But what I did do was so simple, it was just more inconvenient than complicated. I had already gathered much of the information needed to get myself better, and I worked on the assumption that at least some of that information would be the same for the kitten.

We started. What we did was manually create what I have coined DISH, or Defensive Individual Shield Hypothesis. DISH is the name I gave the outer coating on the surface of our skin that we cannot see. More specifically, it is about the frequency this coating is giving off. In a nutshell, I believe this coating enables the body to sort Good Guys the body needs from Bad Guys the body is fighting, especially during times of high inflammation.

When the body is sorting properly, this coating acts like an Exit Ramp. A place for Good Guys to leave to avoid being grouped with Bad Guys and sent through the lymphatic system. If the body is failing to sort, the number of Good Guys the body can actually keep, and how many of the Bad Guys it is able to get rid of becomes a problem. I have figured out a way around this problem.

Okay, let's think about the main concept: batches. A batch is just a group of Bad Guys and Good Guys. Focusing on batches is how I helped my body to sort. There are three ways these batches can be formed. For kitty here, I focused on two of those ways initially: exposure and proximity.

What does this mean? Simple.

For exposure, I thought about the kitten's surroundings. I thought about everything the kitten was being exposed to in its environment. We want to keep it consistent. It was pretty easy to do this for the most part because of the isolation in the dark bedroom. But we needed to include her medicine and her food in this environment. So, we would keep the used feeding bottle next to her in between her meals. We would also wipe a small amount of the medicine from the dropper onto a piece of tissue and place this next to her as well. By doing this, she did not have to sort the medicine, nor the food, from the pneumonia she was trying to fight.

These items would act like the Exit Ramps I mentioned earlier. The presence of these Exit Ramps is what makes DISH work. It is a way for the body to allow the Good Guys to exit the body so they are not grouped with the Bad Guys they are fighting. For most people I believe this is automatic. For some of us though, I think DISH malfunctioning is what makes these Good Guys and Bad Guys become mixed. This mixing, I believe, causes chronic inflammation and nutritional deficiencies.

We did this first step for kitty, but I wanted to be even more proactive. I wanted to give her the biggest leg up possible. This is when I thought of proximity batches.

In a proximity situation, we want to help the areas of her body that the Bad Guy is located. We also want to help the detox organs and her gut (antibiotics kill good bacteria needed there). This works for the same reason as the previous batch. Same concept, just different items to consider. I gathered the nutritional supplements I currently had in the house which were needed for the kidneys, liver, lungs, and gut, and I placed them within a couple of inches of her to start with. She began eating more. About twice as much as she had been, but not the amount she needed.

"I think she is still missing something, Mom," said my kids.

"You're right, and I bet I know what it is."

Since the kitten was on antibiotics, from my past, I had learned that antibiotics disturb the gut's natural balance. I had also learned about how there is a relationship between oxytocin and the gut.[i] Did I remember what this relationship was? No. Did I understand the connection? No. But I remembered it was important to know. We frequently hear that the gut is the second brain after all.

I also recently learned how a preservative used in medical injections mimicked oxytocin on the spleen.[ii] She did recently receive an injection to fight her pneumonia. Did it have this particular preservative in it? Another thing that I did not know. But if her DISH was indeed failing to sort Good Guys from Bad Guys, there was a chance that a third type of batch was involved—a mimicker batch. It was enough to try a Hail Mary. I took the diluted oxytocin spray I had been using for myself and sprayed some on her head and rubbed it on her tummy.

"Mom, look!" My daughter saw it too.

No name Kitty visibly had more energy within minutes of having it placed on her. Why? My belief is that placing a trace amount of this oxytocin on the outside of her body created the Exit Roads this hormone needed in order to not be grouped with the infection she was trying to fight. This Exit Road was making it possible for her to sort the Bad Guy from this Good Guy. It stopped her body from needlessly losing this hormone. By stopping the loss, her hormones were going up. This manual DISH prevented the Good Guy from being grouped with the illness. It enabled her to start using oxytocin as intended. These Exit Roads were the manual DISH.

Even though we just fed her, we thought, let's try again, and she ate all of it! Her tummy became distended, and she slept well. She slept until we had to wake her for her next meal and medication. Rinse and repeat. After two full meals in a row, we were excited. She was finally eating the amount she needed. She ate with vengeance too, which in turn wiped her out for another long nap. Forward progress, finally.

She won...our hearts. What a fighter. We knew we weren't going to be able to give her to Daisy when she returned home.

I guess we needed to give her a name.

6

Kitty Earns a Name

Picking a name…do we give her a name related to who she is or what we believe she can become? We thought of many, we even tested a few out. Christmas Cat was one of them. C.C. for short. Yuck. It just didn't fit her, even though her personality wasn't really known yet because she was sleeping all the time. She was busy healing, growing, and getting better.

We ended up giving the name Moxie a try. When we hear the word Moxie, it conveys confidence, power, and assertiveness. None of which she was, but the name seemed to fit. We ended up looking up the definition before deciding to keep it. When we realized Moxie meant courage, determination, and tackling challenges head on in the face of adversity, we could picture her as tiny, as she was, trying to stick up for herself and staying alive until we found her. She was also proving herself to be a fighter that defies all odds, and she still is. Yes, the kitten needed a name and it needed to be Moxie.

My husband laughed at the name the kids and I settled on. He could only see her current condition. (My husband would later agree with us that it was a good name choice.) Yes, it did look like she was going to be a blind, sickly creature for her duration here on Earth. We were also still unsure if this duration would be short or long. However, we at least had hope now. We all had our fingers crossed that she was past the worst.

The more she ate, the longer she took the medication, and the more her swollen eye seemed to reduce in size. And the more the swelling went down, the more she used her better eye. She also started to be awake more. Remember when I said two kittens are great but only one was more work? Well, the more awake she was, the more alone she felt. We had to go about our day, but she still could not be allowed out of her darkness. She started to get mean. She was definitely getting cabin fever. She needed companionship. She needed someone to knead her, to caress her—to just be with her.

My daughter and I ended up making sure we were taking turns being with her in her isolation. We tried to avoid her being alone for more than two hours at a time. This helped immensely. The tiger that was emerging subsided.

It soon became very apparent she was going to get to keep her left eye. There was much rejoicing. The swelling was even going down on the other eye too. It had almost no swelling at all, especially compared to how bad it had been. Then one day...

"Mom! She opened her bad eye," my daughter squealed from the other room.

"No way."

Sure enough, I could see the eyeball. She actually had both of her eyes open.

Fast forward a few days, and the medicine had run out. I could see her bad eye beginning to swell again. It was starting to look like the infection was returning. I recognized it. It looked just like my caesarean scar when it became infected many years ago. I bet if we could get just a few more days of the antibiotic, we would be able to get this eye working fine. I called to ask for a refill, but they wanted to see her first. Understandable. I jumped through their hoops. I strongly believed that if she just kept with the medication, her eye would be like it was two days ago. But they did not refill it until two days later! Four days for the infection to take root again. Four days for it to get the kind of stronghold that it did not have a few days prior.

When the antibiotics were finally refilled, I was still hoping it would turn out okay. But in my gut, I knew it was too late.

7

Gold Stars for Moxie

Moxie was so entertaining. She was allowed to start being everywhere in the house in spite of her eye being swollen again. She was particularly fond of the toys that made noise.

She was doing so well that my daughter and I thought it would be safe to leave her home alone, but in her room. Up to this point, we tried to always have one of us home.

We were only gone for a couple of hours, but when we got home, she was hiding in my daughter's closet. She thought she'd done something bad. We don't know what she did, but we do know what we saw.

On the right side of her face, around the newly swollen eye from the delayed medication, something that looked like a popped water balloon filled with blood appeared. There was orange-tinted blood everywhere. As we would later learn, the blood was from the lining of the eye rupturing. The eye was still there but the use of it was gone.

The feeling of frustration from them not heeding what I was saying when I wanted the antibiotics to be continuous struck a strong chord with me, leading to a lot of pent-up anger. I had to fight for the self-control to not lash out with my feelings. Of course, the line we were fed was that at least she was able to keep one eye, while they ignored the fact that the option of keeping both was a strong possibility. They had decided on the scenario because they had seen it many times before. They were suspecting that I may not have *really* seen the bad eye as I thought I did. They were not convinced that the eye was ever functional.

What was done was done. It wasn't neglect on anyone's part, but just a standstill of two opinions, where the one with the bigger title outranked the one with the more personal information of the current situation. At this point, we had to accept her fate of being one-eyed.

I was probably deeper in my thoughts than I should have been on the short drive home. Kitty's experience was so similar to my health challenges. But why was it okay if it goes south while having medical professionals involved? While on the same note, if I chose to not take their advice and the same results happened, it was my fault? Do they actually think I care less about the cat (or myself) than they do? They assume we have lack of knowledge when it is actually more like a lack of trust. I think the days of blindly trusting those in white coats, who get paid for services rendered regardless of whether there are favorable results, is coming to an end. A service business where payment is expected regardless of the quality of the service? What other business is allowed to get away with that?

Though she lost one eye, we did know she was going to make it. We continued making sure that any medications she took were also kept near her. We didn't need to rub her tummy and spray her head anymore with the diluted oxytocin spray. We just left it in my daughter's room where she still was most of the time, probably from habit.

We still had her pile of supplements grouped together on the floor, and we noticed she tended to go lay down next to them once in a while. By doing this, her Good Guy nutrients were less likely to be depleted through rejection (No Exit Ramps). I am basically Altering Fields to Enable Recovery (AFTER), manually making her DISH (Defensive Individual Shield Hypothesis) work for her by controlling her environment. These two concepts are my new perspective on chronic inflammation and nutritional deficiency.

When Moxie went in for her next checkup, the staff were so amazed at how healthy she was. The vet even said she never would have believed Moxie had such a rough start if she hadn't seen it herself.

She went on to say, "No, I'm serious. Not even considering all of her problems, she is healthier than any healthy kitten. The healthiest kitten I think I have ever seen, outside of the bad eye." *You mean what might have been avoided if you had believed me?*

The vet proceeded to get permission from me to show her off to all the staff who saw her during her first visit. I was enjoying my sigh of relief. No need for eye surgery. The idea had been bounced back and forth many times over the past few weeks. Awesome. But then the vet started talking about how the next step would be to schedule her to be neutered. She suggested waiting a little until she was older and bigger before doing so. I wasn't sure if I even wanted the procedure done. She was going to be a 100% indoor cat, so was it really necessary? I was looking at it like she was a dog. It isn't that big of a deal, is it?

Little did I know about cat's being in heat!

8

Moxie Wants a Boyfriend

I think this chapter is a chapter I would rather skip, but here it goes anyway. Since cats are almost like rabbits in my eyes when it comes to propagating, I could understand the need for this sterilization procedure to be done. We have never owned a non-neutered cat before. I'm sure at this point, if you have had one yourself, you are probably projectile spitting out your coffee just anticipating what this chapter is about.

But you see, this precious little girl was barely at the age when she would normally be leaving her own mother. How aggressively would she really be seeking motherhood, when she was not going to be around any male cats? Nor would she be let loose to roam the streets in search of a sperm donor for that matter. Because of the many things I was learning about this possible DISH, and how it seemed to be so instrumental in Moxie's changing fate, I really was hoping for minimal medical intervention. Besides, after being on antibiotics for so long, I wanted her good gut bacteria to normalize, before we potentially killed it off again with another round that would certainly accompany any surgical procedure. We decided to wait it out.

Well, it began early. One week we were talking about how she finally drank water from her bowl. How we could finally stop the bottle feedings. How she was now at the age she should be when weaned from her mother. Nice, smooth sailing from here. Right? Wrong.

The following week her crying out began—a continuous meowing as she wandered back and forth through the house late at night. What was she doing? Was she hungry? Was her eye bothering her? After a couple of days of this, she went up to my daughter, laid on her side, and lifted her tail.

"Mom! Moxie is twerking! Gross!!"

"Dang, of course she is. I didn't even think about that. She is barely eight weeks old."

Her hollering at night was her searching for a mate. Okay, now we knew. It went away after a few days.

"Well, that wasn't too bad. If she is only like that once a month, we can handle it."

"I think so," agreed my daughter.

But the following week she started buttering up to my eldest son and getting visibly distraught when he would leave. She was acting like he was a drug hit for her. We suspected her endorphins would fly off the chart when he was here, because she could smell

Tyson (the bully cat) on him every time he came over to visit. My son's siblings would yell at him for petting her and for coming over, because it just made her worse. So, when she was in heat, the eldest son came to the house less frequently.

But, no, that didn't help much. It seemed like maybe only another week had gone by, and I would hear my other son yelling from his bedroom down the hallway, "No, get away from me! I can't help you."

In the beginning, my kids were entertained at having never seen such a transformation of character transpire so quickly before their eyes, and by how it made this otherwise rational animal act psychotic. Of course, being a mom who liked to use object lessons, I suggested they keep that in mind when they hit puberty.

"MOM!!"

"I'm just saying…"

We were always very relieved when it was finally over. If she did this once every four to six weeks, we could deal with it. However, that wasn't the case. It seemed like only a few days, maybe a week, would go by and she would be at it again. Laying on the ground, screaming for company, and moving her tail out of the way as if that must be the only reason her mission wasn't being accomplished. After she went into heat for the third time, the whole family agreed we needed to put her out of her misery; we needed to get her spayed.

I called to make an appointment, and they explained that she needed to not be in heat or recently out of heat in order for the procedure to go well. I told them that they were talking about less than a ten-day window. I think they thought I was exaggerating. I hung up the phone.

When her intensity of twerking and her wallowing screams throughout the night started to subside the fourth go around, we called and made the appointment for the following week.

9

Moxie Survives Surgery

Surgery day arrived. She had come so far up until now.

"Mom, is there anything we can do to make this easier for her?"

"Well, just as a precaution, I guess we could put some minerals and oxytocin on her head." We hadn't needed to do that for quite some time.

We proceeded to rub some on her belly too, since we knew she was going to be getting antibiotics. We were thinking about possible proximity challenges affecting her DISH, and what Good Guys were needed for her gut.

It was so nice seeing her have so much energy, and being so happy to be alive. Chasing her foster sister, sprinting down the hallway, and most of all, playing with her ping pong ball. She loved it. I think it was because not only was it very reactive to the slightest touch, but also because it was easy to hear it on the tile floors as well. I think having one eye caused her to prefer toys she could hear.

The downside to her having all this energy though, was trying to catch her once she saw the carrier. It was becoming significantly more difficult to get those sprawling legs and sharp claws to fit into the carrier so we could get her transported to her destination. That morning, once she had finally been contained, we headed to the veterinarian clinic…once again.

They handed over the paperwork we always had to fill out, reminding us of all the risks involved, and asking if we wanted them to try to resuscitate if things went wrong. Of course, there were no guarantees that the pet would make it. Ugh! Flashbacks to my surgeries. It's like you are being held at knife point and told you have the option to choose what you wish to do. Really? Do we really have a choice? So frustrating.

All the family members would admit that she had been a handful from the time she entered our home just a few months ago. But what we did not expect was, as the day wore on, we were beginning to miss her. When we would normally need to feed her or clean her eye, we had time to get a cup of coffee instead. The coffee didn't taste as good though. We couldn't help worrying if she was under the knife yet, or if she was in recovery. If she was awake. If…

When the vet who did the surgery finally called, he let us know that she was in recovery, awake, and resting. Then he proceeded to say it was more difficult than expected because she was starting to go into heat again. Based on the size of her ovaries, he ventured to guess that she was in constant heat. *We* could have told *him* that!

When we were able to go pick her up at the end of the day, they gave a list of things we should be aware of. For example, we shouldn't let her run, jump, chase or lick her tummy.

"Really?" *You do know she is a kitten, right?*

"Well, if she becomes too active her incisions could tear," he continued to warn us.

"You might want to consider getting a large indoor dog cage for her to be in for a couple of days."

"We'll keep an eye on her." Meanwhile I'm thinking, *That would have been nice to know before we had her go in for surgery.*

Moxie, in her carrier, was brought out of the back of the office to the room we were waiting in. She started meowing the second she heard my daughter's voice. I don't think she stopped loudly protesting until she was home and out of her carrier once more.

10

Moxie Hits a Roadblock

We got Moxie home and brought her inside. However, in an effort to control her environment in her weakened state, we left her in her carrier just inside the door for ten minutes. By doing this, her frequency adjusted from the carrier to the carrier and the house. After those ten minutes, letting her out would now mean that she only needed to focus on the different frequencies in the home.

This may sound a little confusing, but it is a system I have named Altering Fields to Enable Recovery (AFTER). From studying and discovering DISH, I have learned to implement many different procedures to enable myself to manually alter my DISH when it is not doing its job automatically. By taking these steps, symptoms reduced significantly, and I was able to feel better before *I was* better.

Meanwhile, back to Moxie's return.

Nemo, who had pretty much reclaimed her domain in my daughter's room, emerged. She went to the carrier and sniffed at Moxie, almost as if trying to calm her down. It caused the incessant meowing to cease. Nemo was glad to see her new sister home again. But, oh boy, when Nemo turned to walk away and Moxie was unable to follow, she began meowing almost in a state of panic as she frantically clawed at the latch to be set free.

We let her out. And the second we did, she calmed down again. But we needed to keep her calm. How? To keep her from running. How? We decided to see how long this would work. We could tell she was obviously sore, so hopefully that would be enough to keep her somewhat subdued until it was okay to be active again. A few times I would find myself holding my breath as she eyed a window ledge contemplating jumping up. The first few times, she walked away. So far so good.

Moxie was allowed water the first night, but she could not start eating until the following day.

At this point I should mention that she was a naughty baby sister. She should normally have been eating her kitten food, while her big foster sister ate adult cat food. Well, in Moxie's eyes, obviously she was getting the short end of the deal; Nemo's food must have been better.

Because of this, when we fed her the small amount as required the following morning, we didn't think much of it when she threw it back up shortly after. We suspected that she ate too much too soon because she probably ate some of her sister's food too. We would have to just guard Nemo's bowl more closely.

In the evening, she was sick again, and I felt sorry for her. She was just a baby. She acted just like my kids used to when they were toddlers. She knew when she was going to be sick, and it didn't matter where she, or I, was in the house when she was about to be sick, she would come running to me like I could help make it stop. Her meowing sounded frantic and scared and was quickly followed up by the emptying of her tummy. She would then run away immediately afterwards. I think she thought she was in trouble for what she just did.

Should I be concerned? She was having urine releases and bowel movements, so she wasn't clogged. Those were the symptoms we were supposed to watch for. They said nothing about throwing up. What was going on? What should we do?

Did something happen during surgery?

Was it something major or minor? Did we need to call the vet?

Or was it just something interfering with her DISH sorting again?

Did our precautionary measures work or not work?

Would she have been even worse off if we hadn't been proactive?

Well, we may never know the answers to those questions, but we could test to see if her DISH was failing to sort again.

I know of a way to find out.

11

Manual DISH for Moxie Again

Talk about history repeating itself. Instead of trying to get her to eat now, it was trying to get her food to stay in. Different problem but with the same end result.

When she was unable to keep her breakfast down also, I decided to try to help her make a manual DISH again. I did not know what was interfering with her DISH, but I did know that I could help her with her exposure batch. I would start with her next meal that evening. If it didn't work, I would call the veterinarian office in the morning.

Other than being unable to keep her food down, she seemed fine. We had done the best we could in limiting her activeness. She was drinking water and keeping it down. I wondered if, when she ate, her food gave her the nutrients she needed to fight her virus, infection, or whatnot. If her immune system was already burdened, maybe this food 'fighting for her' was causing too much inflammation. Maybe the food (Good Guy) was becoming mixed with whatever Bad Guy was causing the problem. Note: I didn't know who the Bad Guy was, but it didn't really matter. The key was to keep the Good Guys in by making Exit Ramps for them.

When supper time came around, instead of using a cup to scoop out her serving, I used my hand. The dry cat food was oily and bits of it would stick to the oil and to my hand. That was part of the plan. I took my soiled hand and rubbed it on the top of her head, on her tummy, and down her back just two or three times to try to get it everywhere.

Doing this made the Exit Ramp. Just think equal sign. Her cat food was now on the outside and inside of her body: equal. So, if eating her food was helping her to fight a Bad Guy that was in her, at least now it would not become tied to this Bad Guy. This Bad Guy she was fighting could have been a virus, her prior residual pneumonia, or even the drugs she had to have put in her for her surgery.

Whatever Bad Guy it was that was causing her to reject her food was now what I call The Target. This equal sign of food being on the outside and inside of her body was preventing the food from being grouped with the Bad Guy (The Target). I was giving the food, and the Good Guys in it, an exit route to take. Something was happening when she ate her food. I was just allowing her to focus on the 'something' instead of the 'something' *and* her food.

Did she keep her food down? Yes.

Did I repeat it every time I fed her? Yes.

I did it for about a week. Did she keep her food down every time? Yes.

Did I stop doing it? Yes.

Did she keep her food down still? NO!

I went back to doing it for another week, and when I thought about how scared she sounded just before vomiting, I decided to go an extra few days. I stopped. She threw up.

I decided to just continually do this for twenty days. It was usually how long it took when I needed to do this for myself.

I would test her DISH after the twenty days to see if I needed to continue doing it. I did this by not wiping the food on her for one meal. If she couldn't keep her food down, I knew I needed to continue with her manual DISH. She ended up needing to go sixty days. Did it eventually work? Yes.

Do I need to keep doing it still? No.

If at some point she wasn't 'acting her normal self,' I would go ahead and repeat the process of just rubbing some of it on her back. Why? Because my motto is prevention is so much easier than correction. And if it is this simple, why not just do it?

How powerful is it to have this information in our hands? And just look how something so simple can make such a big difference.

12

My Little Advocate for DISH

I can understand how hard it is to grasp how something so simple can be so powerful. I have seen it firsthand so many times myself, and I still have a hard time believing what a difference it makes. But it is what I do on a daily basis now to feel better before *I am* better. I think this information is so important that I have written a book about this groundbreaking hypothesis of a complementary body system. *Health Backwards: An Original Look from a Different Perspective* explains how I discovered it, what its functions are, the health consequences when malfunctioning, and how I addressed those challenges.

As I continue to write my books and courses, to share what I have learned about my DISH concept, Moxie keeps me company. I have a box on my desk which she seems to always be in when I am there typing. If for some reason I miss my morning time of writing, she goes wandering through the house looking for me and meowing at me until I take my seat. I know she doesn't know what I'm writing about, but I bet she would back me on the concept working. She is living proof. I am living proof too.

Sometimes I wonder if she is grateful. I see her lounging in her box looking out the window. I see her lying on the windowsill next to her new sister. She is fascinated by the outside world, but she has no desire to be a part of it. The saying of 'the grass is greener on the other side' applies here. She is basking in her greener grass. She has no desire to reenter the Bad Land past those doors.

Sometimes I wonder if she was brought into our life so I could test my hypothesis one last time, to gain the confidence I needed to share what I have discovered.

Okay, maybe we did need another cat. I just didn't know it.

Parting Thoughts

A few things I would like to make clear. There are always at least two sides to everything. People can only make decisions based on what they know or what they have been trained to do. I think the vet did a great job. It was clear she cared about the kitten, was knowledgeable in her field, and had good people skills. How could I judge her for something I discovered, and she didn't know about? It would have taken way too much time to explain my DISH concept to her. Plus, she may not have wanted to hear it.

This is why I wrote *Health Backwards*. Sometimes people would ask me what I was doing about my health. The concept is easy, but trying to explain it when so much information builds upon previous information is time consuming. Now, I can direct them to my book and have different conversations, instead of having to be a broken record repeating myself so much. It also enabled me to serve my information to far more people with them having the option of choosing to take a bite or not. I just need to serve it. It's up to each individual whether they would like to partake. I've done my job.

Meet the Author

Cyndi earned her Bachelor of Science degree in 1991. She married Ron in 1992, served a short term as a commissioned Air Traffic Control officer in the Air Force, then became a stay-at-home mom.

Cyndi's parents became pregnant with her at Camp Lejeune. It would be later discovered this Marine base had contaminated water containing many harmful components, including strontium-90 and benzene at levels ranging from 240 to 3,400 times higher than what is permitted by safety standards. In Cyndi's early years, she lived in New Zealand and Turkey. She remained a military dependent until her dad retired when she was in eighth grade.

Find her and sign up for her newsletter at desperatetobewell.com (blog) or cyndiwhatif.com (author site). She is also on LinkedIn, Facebook, and Instagram.

Her book, *Health Backwards: An Original Look from a Different Perspective,* earned an Honorable Mention at The BookFest Fall 2023 awards.

View videos of Moxie at cyndiwhatif.com/moxie.

Other Book

⇨ *Health Backwards: An Original Look from a Different Perspective*
- Her groundbreaking hypothesis of a complementary body system
- Its discovery, functions, health consequences when malfunctioning, and how the author addressed these challenges to overcome her chronic fatigue.

More Books to Come

⇨ *Health Backwards: The Journal*
- A guide for your medical journey.
- Packed with information and questions to use to search for answers.
- It is not medical advice, but a medical tool to help make quicker progress.

⇨ *Health Backwards Part 2: How I Implemented AFTER*
- A detailed look at how I did the procedures I have shared in this book.
- It builds off Health Backwards.

Endnotes

[i] Rodriguez, Ana Maria, Ph.D. "Research Connecting Gut Bacteria and Oxytocin Provides a New Mechanism for Microbiome Promoted Health Benefits." Baylor College of Medicine. November 2, 2023 https://blogs.bcm.edu/2023/11/02/from-the-labs-research-connecting-gut-bacteria-and-oxytocin-provides-a-new-mechanism-for-microbiome-promoted-health-benefits/

[ii] Ayers, A B, B. N. Davies, P. G. Withrington. "Responses of the Isolated, Perfused Human Spleen to Sympathetic Nerve Stimulation, Catecholamines and Polypeptides." National Library of Medicine. January 1972. https://pubmed.ncbi.nlm.nih.gov/4335551/

Buy *Health Backwards* Here.

Or learn more at healthbackwards.com.

Made in the USA
Monee, IL
11 January 2024

50811103R00036